Glen Loates
BIRDS
OF NORTH AMERICA

For Paul & Marn
Kwishing

Glen — 79

Ross James

Glen Loates
BIRDS OF NORTH AMERICA

Cerebrus Publishing Company Limited
Prentice-Hall of Canada, Ltd., Scarborough, Ontario.

Canadian Cataloguing in Publication Data

James, Ross D., 1943-
Glen Loates Birds of North America
ISBN 0-920016-11-1 (Cerebrus)
ISBN 0-13-357103-3 (Prentice-Hall)

1. Birds—Canada—Pictorial works.
2. Birds—United States—Pictorial works.
I. Loates, Glen Martin. II. Title.
QL674.J35   598.2'0971   C79-094466-9

Introduction

The paintings
of Glen Loates, plus the profiles and maps of
breeding distribution, are intended to contribute
to a better understanding of some of our birds and the
role they play in the scheme of living things. No
other animals give us such a wealth of opportunity
for recreation and enjoyment, not to mention
considerable benefit to mankind.
Warblers fly thousands of miles each year to search
branches and leaves for the food which sustains them and their
young, but are unable to understand why the trees grow.
However, man, in his wisdom, cannot ignore this interrelationship
of animal and environment. By studying creatures such as birds,
we learn of the ways of nature which also affect our
relationship to the world. By providing for these creatures,
we indirectly provide for ourselves. For if the world becomes
so barren and polluted that the birds cannot survive,
then man will soon follow them into extinction.

Ross D. James

List of Plates

Common Loon
Gavia immer

This is one of only four species of loon.
The powerful legs of the Common Loon are set far back on their bodies making them very capable
swimmers, but they can hardly walk when out of the water. They cannot take off from land, and even
on water must patter along the surface, half flying, half running, for a long distance before
becoming airborne. Once aloft, however, strong, steady, rapid wingbeats
propel them quickly through the air.
In the breeding season they can be found across the Northern Hemisphere from Alaska to Iceland,
and south to northern United States. Once very common, with one or more pair on almost
every lake, their numbers have decreased, apparently due to the effect of chemical
insecticides on reproduction.
Fish is their main diet, plus frogs, clams, leeches, insects
and aquatic vegetation.
Loons gather large piles of wet, half-rotted reeds and vegetable material for use as nests. They are
heaped in the water near or on shore, but never far from the water. The nest is about
two feet across with a shallow depression for the eggs. Both parents incubate
the eggs which are a dark olive brown, sparingly marked with
dark brown spots.
Young loons leave the nest shortly after hatching. Although good swimmers from birth, they often ride
on the backs of their parents. The young are covered with a thick black down at hatching. Feathers
begin to replace the down by two weeks of age. The family group remains together until
August or September when the young are fully feathered and able to fly. At this time adults,
which have identical plumage, begin to molt from their bright black and white summer
plumage to a drab, unmarked gray winter plumage, closely resembling
that of the immature birds.
In autumn they migrate south, spending the winter chiefly in salt water along both coasts of North
America south to the Gulf Coast and Baja, California. By February the adult birds begin to
molt back to their striking summer plumage, but the young do not. They take two years
to mature and remain in the wintering areas until they assume the adult plumage
in preparation for their return to the northern lakes.
Loons return each year as soon as the ice leaves the lakes. A pair, which may remain mated for life,
can return to the same lake for many years. Everyone who has camped in boreal forest areas
is familiar with their mournful cries and weird "laughing" ringing through
the morning mists or the dusk of evening.

Total length: Males 710-890mm (28-35in). Females 690-810mm (27-32in)
Wing length: Males 340-380mm (13-15in). Females 315-360mm (12.5-14in)
Wing span: Males 1075-1520mm (42.5-60in). Females 1080-1400mm (42.5-55in)
Weight: Males 2900-3800g (6.4-8.4lbs). Females 2800-3600g (6.2-7.9lbs)

Breeding dates: May-July
Incubation period: 29 days
Number of eggs: 2 (1-3)

Preferred habitat: Lakes

Snow Goose
Chen caerulescens

These are birds of the high arctic, nesting in isolated areas across the continent north of the forests. They are a familiar sight as migrant birds forming large V formations or long thin wavy lines passing high overhead in spring and autumn as they move to and from wintering areas in the United States.

The Snow Goose has two color phases: white, as suggested by the common name, and blue as suggested by the scientific name *caerulescens*. Until recently these two color phases were considered separate species. We now know that the two types interbreed and goslings of both colors can be found in the same nest. Early in this century blue birds were much rarer and no one knew where they nested, but the blue colored birds have increased in numbers and spread westward through almost the whole population of this species.

Snow Geese feed almost entirely on vegetable matter, mainly roots and green tops of grasses, sedged and a variety of aquatic plants. They are fond of winter wheat in wintering areas. Small molluscs and a variety of marine invertebrates may be consumed in seaside areas.

The nest is a slight depression in the ground and formed of small amounts of grasses and twigs gathered immediately about the nest. This is lined with a gray colored down to insulate the eggs in the arctic environment. The eggs are white when laid, but soon become stained in the nest. The female incubates the eggs alone and seldom leaves the nest throughout the incubation period, living mainly off reserves of stored fat. The young leave the nest soon after hatching. The arctic nesting season is so short that only one attempt at nesting is possible if the young are to be old enough to fly before freeze-up in the autumn.

The young are covered with a thick coat of down upon hatching. This is a slaty bluish color in birds which are to be blue phase birds, or a pale yellow and olive yellow down on white phase birds. By autumn migration the immature birds have acquired a plumage which is somewhat like that of adults, but the white feathers are mottled and washed with brownish gray. These dusky markings gradually disappear over winter until there is little left of the immature plumage by their first summer. During a complete molt in summer, with the adults, they acquire a nearly fully adult plumage. The young do not breed until at least two years of age.

The young grow rapidly and begin to fly after about a month and a half. Before autumn migration large flocks gather in staging areas to graze and fatten up before the long flight south.

Total length: Males 685-790mm (27-31in). Females 665-750mm (26-30in)
Wing length: Males 405-470mm (16-18in). Females 385-430mm (15-17in)
Wing span: Males 1380-1540mm (54-60in). Females 1360-1510mm (53-59in)
Weight: Males 1875-3060g (4lb3oz-6lb12oz). Females 1980-2500g (4lb6oz-5lb8oz)

Breeding dates: June
Incubation period: 22-23 days
Number of eggs: 4-5 (2-8)

Preferred habitat: Marshes, wet fields

Harlequin Duck

Histrionicus histrionicus

The beautifully patterned
Harlequin males with the less vividly colored females spend their winters near the sea coasts on
both sides of the continent. The birds on each coast belong to different subspecies, but they differ only
slightly in color and size. About the rocky shores they feed amid the pounding surf. In summer they move
inland to breed along the shores and on islands in swiftly flowing mountain streams. Here they are
equally adept at swimming and diving for food in the turbulent waters. In the streams their food
consists largely of aquatic insects and their larvae. Small fish, fish eggs, frogs, tadpoles, crayfish,
clams and snails are also eaten. On the sea coast, mussels and other shellfish, with small
crabs, insects and fish are the main foods, as well as some aquatic plants.
Nests are usually placed a short distance from the shores of rivers or lakes, where they can
be concealed at the base of bushes and shrubs. Dry grasses form the nest which is lined well with an olive brown
down. The eggs are a light buff or cream color. Incubation is performed solely by the female who is left
to rear the brood alone. The young leave the nest shortly after hatching and are excellent swimmers,
soon able to navigate in swift rough water nearly as well as the adults.
The downy young are a brownish color above, with white undersides and a white cheek patch.
This is molted through the summer to an immature plumage which looks much like that of adult females.
The immature plumage is retained until the end of their second summer. The males then begin,
through the autumn, to molt to an adult plumage for the beginning of their third summer.
They do not breed until at least two years of age and probably most
spend their second summer at sea.
Several broods of young birds may group together after hatching to form a crèche.
The young are able to fly by about six weeks of age, but those hatched near the sea may simply float
downstream to their wintering areas while still flightless.

Total length: Males 405-535mm (16-21in). Females 370-430mm (14.5-17in)
Wing length: Males 190-210mm (7.5-8.25in). Females 175-205mm (6.75-8in)
Wing span: Males: 610-710mm (24-28in). Females 585-635mm (23-25in)
Weight: Males 635-770g (22-27oz). Females 520-595g (18-21g)

Breeding dates: May-July
Incubation period: 27-29 days
Number of eggs: 3-7

Preferred habitat: Mountain streams, rocky shores

Harlequin Ducks

Water movement

Red-tailed Hawk
Buteo jamaicensis

These widespread and best-known
hawks in North America, use their broad, rounded wings
to soar on rising air currents.
Their food consists mostly of mice, squirrels, rabbits and other rodents. They also frequently eat snakes,
frogs, skunks, crayfish and insects. Only occasionally are they guilty of the attacks on poultry, game
birds or other small birds for which they have been unjustly persecuted. They are actually a most
beneficial species because of the numerous rodents they consume, and usually hunt by soaring
high over open country, depending on their acute vision to spot even
a tiny mouse far below in the grass.
They also hunt to some extent in the forest edges and woodlots where they nest. The nest, which
is placed high in most any species of tree, is built of sticks lined with strips of bark and
usually a few sprigs of fresh green pine, cedar or hemlock. If not disturbed, it may
be used in successive years.
Red-tailed hawks winter as far north as southern Canada and may establish territories and repair or
build nests in mid-winter. The eggs are a dull white, sparingly spotted with brown tones.
Only the female incubates the eggs, but the male brings food for her
and the young when they hatch.
The young are covered with a long, soft buff-white down at hatching, and this is replaced quickly with
a whiter and woolier down. When the young leave the nest after about four weeks, they are nearly
full-grown and fully-feathered. At this time they look much like the adults except they lack
the reddish tail. They begin to molt in early spring to an adult plumage, but this molt is
not complete until late summer or early fall. Adults also molt once a year, beginning
in spring and lasting through summer.
The Red-tailed is one hawk which has adjusted well to man's activities, perhaps even benefitting from
the extensive clearing of forests for farm lands. Its harsh, rasping scream will hopefully remain
a familiar sound for generations.

Total length: Males 470-560mm (18.5-22in). Females 530-610mm (21-24in)
Wing length: Males 340-390mm (13.5-15.5in). Females 355-440mm (14-17in)
Wing span: Males 1095-1300mm (43-51in). Females 1185-1370mm (46.5-54in)
Weight: Males 635-1200g (1.4-2.6lbs). Females 660-1480g (1.5-3.3lbs)

Breeding dates: March-July
Incubation period: 28-32 days
Number of eggs: 2-4

Preferred habitat: Open country, woodlots

Ring-necked Pheasant
Phasianus colchicus

There are no true pheasants native to North America. Ring-necked pheasants originally ranged only through central Asia, from the Ukraine to China and Japan. All those in North America are descended from stock introduced in the late 19th century. The birds proved well-adapted to the climate of the northern United States and spread rapidly across the country. From coast to coast they now occupy the northern half of the United States and the extreme south of Canada.

Their diet consists of insects, weed seeds, nuts, wild fruit and berries, grains and occasionally other cultivated crops. Many of the insects eaten are crop pests and most of the grain is picked from the ground after harvest. Only rarely are they responsible for damage to crops.

Pheasants seek food and cover in the brushy borders of fields, marshes, woodlots and overgrown pastures. The courtship call of the males is a loud "crow" accompanied by rapid wing flapping. This crowing also delineates the territorial boundaries where the brilliantly plumaged males strut and display to the females. Each male may court from one to three females. Only those females with mottled brown plumage build the nests and incubate the eggs. When sitting still, the females are very well camouflaged and one may walk close to an incubating bird without being aware of it. In fact, they rely so heavily on their protective coloration that they refuse to leave a nest until almost stepped upon.

The nest is built on the ground among the grass of fields, fencerows or roadsides, rarely far from water. It is a small depression lined with grass or leaves. The eggs are a rich brownish-olive color with a slight gloss. The newly-hatched chicks leave the nest as soon as their down has dried. The mother then leads them about looking for food and brooding them at night or in cold or storm. After several weeks the male bird may join a family group, but ordinarily the female raises the brood alone.

The chicks all hatch at about the same time and are covered with a yellowish down lined and spotted with browns and blacks. This bright down is quickly replaced with a somber brown, not unlike that of the female. This plumage, in turn, changes to an adult one in late summer and fall when adults also molt their feathers. By late autumn all birds are in an adult plumage.

When flushed, pheasants are capable of swift, strong flight from the area of danger. Yet they much prefer to walk or run. Spending most of their time on the ground, they are incapable of flying over long distances. They remain in the same areas year round and, throughout their life, do not wander perhaps farther than 10 miles from their birth place.

Total length: Males 750-940mm (29.5-37in). Females 610-660mm (24-26in)
Wing length: Males 225-260mm (9-10in). Females 210-220mm (8-9in)
Wing span: Males 785-840mm (31-33in). Females 700-750mm (27.5-29.5in)
Weight: Males 1000-1560g (2.2-3.4lbs). Females 825-1100g (1.8-2.4lbs)

Breeding dates: April-July
Incubation period: 23-25 days
Number of eggs: 8-15

Preferred habitat: Farmland

Ring-necked pheasant

GLOATES

Barn Owl

Tyto alba

ound around the world, there are about 34 subspecies on all major continents except Antarctica. They range everywhere except in the north and on high mountains where boreal forest conditions prevail, and on oceanic islands. They are distinguished from all other owls by their heart-shaped facial pattern, and their long legs and wings which extend behind the tail.

Owls have long been persecuted as birds of ill omen and perhaps none more than Barn Owls. They often nest in abandoned buildings as well as barns, and have caused many reports of haunted houses. Their loud harsh screams and growling noises in the dead of night are sufficiently terrifying to create thoughts of ghosts and haunted places.

Yet no owl deserves more protection for its beneficial activities as it is the most efficient living mouse trap. Almost its entire diet consists of various species of rodents considered destructive to agricultural crops and fruit trees. So good is its hearing that by sound alone it can locate and capture mice rustling in the grass on the darkest of nights.

The Barn Owl is not a bird of the forests, but finds its best supply of food in open fields or around barns, granaries and other buildings. It is also more strictly nocturnal than other owls, remaining hidden in hollow trees, caves, burrows, attics and barns until after dark. Such places also serve as nesting sites. Apparently no nest is constructed. The eggs are simply deposited on the ground or floor where it roosts. However, if a site is used over a number of years, the numerous pellets of cast bones and fur which are scattered about the roost may form a platform on which the eggs are laid.

The eggs are a pure white color without luster. The shell is finely granulated and the eggs are generally more pointed than those of other owls. They are laid at intervals of two or three days and are incubated – only by the female – from the time the first egg is laid. Consequently the young hatch at similar intervals of two or three days and vary greatly in size.

The newly-hatched owls are covered with white down that is soon replaced by one which is thick, wooly and buffy-white. From this they molt to their first winter plumage which is nearly complete when the birds leave the nest. This first winter plumage is essentially the same as the adult plumage. Females are about equal to or slightly larger than males, but have similar plumage colors.

Adults molt once a year in late summer and autumn.

Barn Owls are permanent residents throughout most of their range. They may wander considerably in the autumn, and in winter may move from the northern parts of their range.

Total length: Males 360-430mm (14-17in). Females 365-440mm (14.5-17.5in)
Wing length: Males 315-330mm (12.5-13in). Females 310-340mm (12-13.5in)
Wing span: Males 1000-1110mm (39-44in). Females 900-1130mm (35.5-44.5in)
Weight: Males 275-600g (.6-1.3lbs). Females 250-660g (.5-1.5lbs)

Breeding dates: March-July
Incubation period: 30-34 days
Number of eggs: 6-10

Preferred habitat: Open fields

Barn Owl

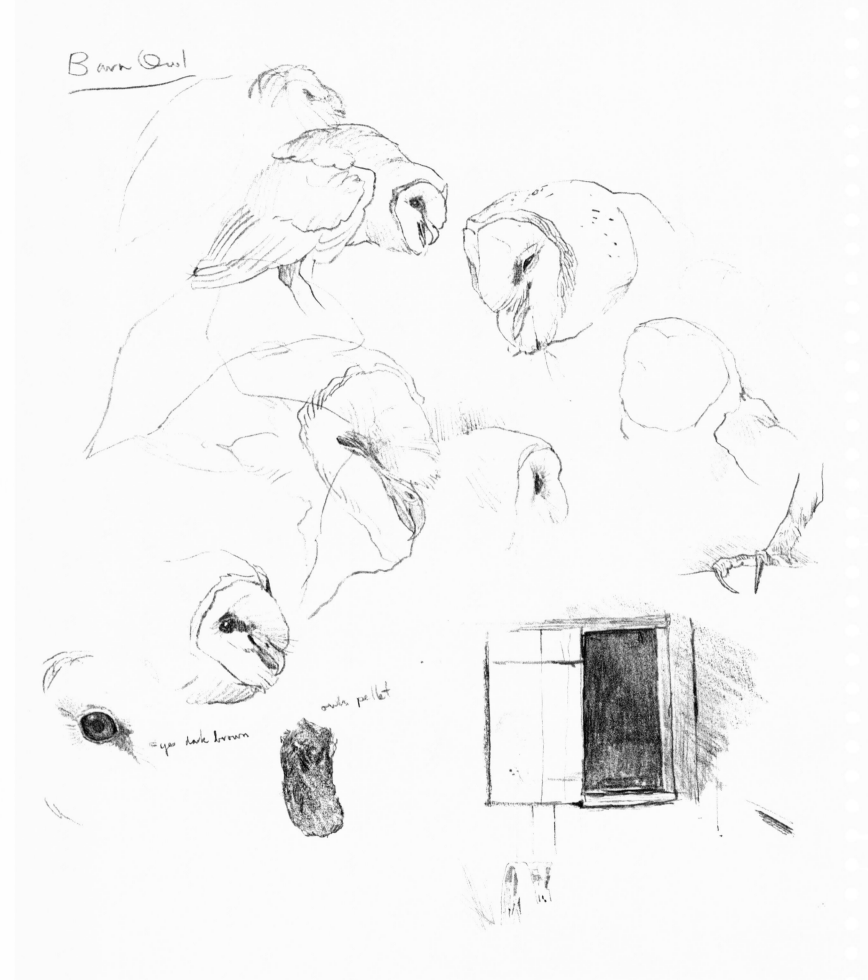

eyes dark brown

owls pellet

Screech Owl
Otus asio

This is one of the best known
small owls as it occupies much of the populated areas of North America. However, it is probably known
more by sound than sight as it is predominately nocturnal, remaining concealed by day in a natural
tree cavity, a building, or the dense branches of an evergreen. But it often occupies woodlots or
old orchards near human dwellings and even city gardens.
Screech Owls feed mainly on small mammals and birds. Using their keen hearing as well as their eyes,
they are able to catch an assortment of mice, rats, and shrews on the ground. They also take crayfish,
snakes, lizards, scorpions, and even earthworms. In addition they catch a great many insects including
large moths, beetles, grasshoppers, cutworms, and crickets either in the air or on the ground.
While they prefer rodents, they take a number of birds – mostly pigeons, starlings and
house sparrows where these are abundant.
The nests are usually natural cavities in trees or abandoned woodpecker holes, often close to the ground.
The pure white eggs are laid on whatever wood chips or other material may be in the cavity.
Incubation is by the female only, while the male provides food. The eggs, laid at intervals
of two or three days, may be incubated from the time the first one is laid or after several
have been laid. Thus the young may be various ages in the same nest.
When hatched the young are covered with a white down. This is quickly replaced with a pale grayish- or
cinnamon-colored downy plumage, reflecting the adult colors that will come later. The wings and
tail grow in quickly, and throughout the summer the winter plumage replaces the downy
plumage over the body. This winter plumage, resembling that of adult birds,
is retained until the annual molt the following summer.
The mottled plumage of adult Screech Owls in eastern North America is either reddish or gray.
Coloration is independent of sex, age, or season, and provides excellent protection
as these owls perch near a tree trunk during the day.

Total length: Males 215-250mm (8.5-9.8in). Females 220-260mm (8.7-10.2in)
Wing length: Males 155-175mm (6.1-6.9in). Females 155-180mm (6.1-7.1in)
Wing span: Males 535-620mm (21-24.5in). Females 550-620mm (21.5-24.5in)
Weight: Males 125-230g (4.4-8.1oz). Females 150-250g (5.3-8.8oz)

Breeding dates: March-May
Incubation period: 26 days
Number of eggs: 4-5

Preferred habitat: Open woodlands

Eastern Screech Owl

Young in juvenal plumage

foot holding branch

holding prey

hind toe turned to grip branch

wing folded

G L
G

Great Horned Owl

Bubo virginianus

Common to most of North, Central and South America with the exception of the Arctic and Caribbean Islands, about 17 subspecies can be recognized. They vary from light-colored, subarctic birds, nearly as white as Snowy Owls, to very dark forms in the humid, west coast forests.

Usually birds of the forest, they prefer to remain as far from human habitation as possible. One of the largest and most aggressive of owls in the Western Hemisphere, they hunt for almost any creature that walks, crawls, flies or swims, with the exception of the larger mammals. They will even nourish themselves upon other owls, snakes, porcupines, bats and skunks.

In areas where there are no longer extensive forests, these birds will inhabit small woodlots where they may become a nuisance to farmers, attacking chickens or domestic cats. However, numerous rabbits, starlings, pigeons, mice and rats also form part of their diet. They hunt by hearing and sight, both of which are excellent.

These owls, which are resident year round, begin their deep, booming hoots in the middle of winter, heralding the coming of courtship and nesting. They are one of our earliest breeding birds, and the eggs must be constantly brooded to keep them from freezing. Sometimes both the nest and the incubating bird may be completely covered with snow.

Great Horned Owls do not construct their own nests, but take over an old hawk's, crow's or squirrel's nest, or find a hollow tree large enough to accommodate them. A few twigs or pine needles and some down feathers are all that is necessary to complete a nest before the eggs are laid. The white, almost-round eggs are incubated only by the female, but the male provides food for her and the young until the young are old enough to be left alone in the nest.

When hatched, the owlets are covered with a white down. This is soon replaced with a dense buff-colored down which, in turn, is gradually replaced with a darker, downy, buff-colored, juvenal plumage. The latter is worn until the autumn when the first winter plumage appears. This first winter plumage resembles that of the adult, but some of the down may persist, and is retained until the following autumn. At this time, both the owlets and adults molt, with the owlets adopting typical adult plumage. Although both males and females are similarly colored, the female of the species is decidedly larger.

Their flight is as silent as that of other owls and they may hunt during the day as well as at night, in order to feed their hungry offspring. Great Horned Owls are very aggressive in defense of their young, making repeated, swift, silent and violent attacks against any humans attempting to reach a nest. Their large talons – so deadly to rodents – are capable of ripping large gashes in the head and arms of unwary human intruders.

Total length: Males 460-580mm (18-23in). Females 555-640mm (22-25in)
Wing length: Males 320-390mm (12.5-15in). Females 350-400mm (14-16in)
Wing span: Males 1200-1330mm (47-52in). Females 1245-1430mm (49-56in)
Weight: Males 1110-1580g (2.4-3.5lbs). Females 1060-2175g (2.3-4.8lbs)

Breeding dates: February-April
Incubation period: 28-30 days
Number of eggs: 2 (1-5)

Preferred habitat: Woodland

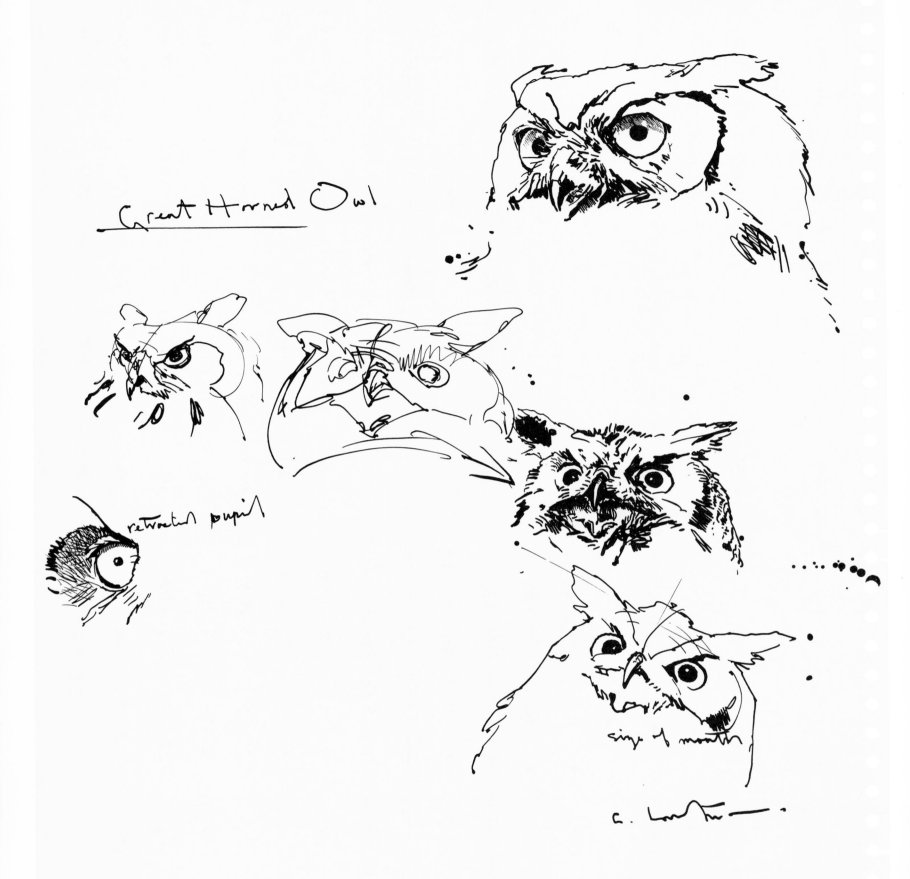

Great Horned Owl

retracted pupil

wing of mouth

C. Lansdowne

Saw-whet Owl
Aegolius acadicus

These tiny owls breed across
Canada, north to southeastern Alaska and southern Hudson Bay, south to the northern United States in the
east and to the Mexican border in the western mountains. However, they are so nocturnal that they are
seldom seen, except perhaps in autumn as they fly southward in small numbers. But as the southern
edge of the winter range is scarcely further south than that of the summer range, the movement
appears to involve mainly birds from the northern parts of their range moving to spend
winter in southern breeding areas. The numbers and extent of this movement vary
with the severity of winter and the availability of food in northern areas.
The Saw-whets eat mainly mice and small rodents, occasionally taking a small bird or a few insects.
They prefer to hunt their prey in the dark, swampy recesses of the coniferous forest. Most often
they roost and hunt within a few feet of the ground. Concealing themselves among
dense foliage by day, they are seldom seen, and except for a few weeks in spring
during mating season, they are seldom heard calling at night.
Most commonly, nests appear to be abandoned woodpecker holes, although other tree cavities may
serve as well. No nesting material is brought to the nest cavity. The pure-white eggs are smooth
and oval, and are deposited right on the wood chips found in such cavities. Since the eggs
are laid at intervals of one to three days and incubated as soon as laid, the young hatch
over a period of time, such that it is not uncommon to find nearly-grown and
newly-hatched young in the same nest.
When hatched the young are covered with a white down. This is gradually replaced until, at about four
weeks of age, they are covered with a soft downy juvenal plumage. The head, except for a white
patch on the forehead, the breast and the back are a rich brown color and the underparts
from the breast down are buff in color. So distinctive is this plumage that
these owls were once thought to be a separate species.
This juvenal plumage is retained throughout most of the summer when a complete molt of contour
feathers provides the young with a plumage which is nearly identical to that of adult birds.
The adults undergo a molt of all feathers through the autumn. The Saw-whet's plumage
is nearly uniform across the continent and only two subspecies are recognized.
The males and females are almost the same in size and appearance.
These owls may be approached to within a few feet and on occasion even captured by hand.
Their name is derived from one of the call notes which can be heard in late winter.
This call, given in sets of three, sounds remarkably like
a file being drawn across a large saw blade.

Total length: Males 180-220mm (7-8.5in). Females 190-215mm (7.5-8.5in)
Wing length: 130-140mm (5-5.5in). Females 130-145mm (5-5.7in)
Wing span: Males 445-480mm (17.5-19in). Females 420-495mm (16.5-19.5in)
Weight: Males 65-120g (2.3-4.2oz). Females 60-100g (2.1-3.5oz)

Breeding dates: April-June
Incubation period: 26-28 days
Number of eggs: 5-6

Preferred habitat: Woodland

Saw-Whet Owl

G. LORTES

Feet from the left side

Feather pattern on back

Saw-Whet Owl

Red-headed Woodpecker
Centurus erythrocephalus

These strikingly handsome birds with boldly patterned markings, are often found along roadsides and are familiar to most people throughout their range in central eastern North America. They were previously more common in farming areas, foraging in the woodlots and using wooden fence posts as nesting sites. Land clearing, clean farming and metal fenceposts have all contributed to reducing their numbers in many areas. The automobile has also taken its toll, for many Red-headed Woodpeckers are killed along the roadsides where they like to feed.

Only in the northern parts of its range is this species migratory. Most remain year round in the open groves and scattered tall trees of open country where they prefer to live. Here they feed on beetles, ants, wasps, grasshoppers, crickets, moths and caterpillars. Many of these insects are secured in flight, as the woodpecker behaves like a flycatcher. However, about half the diet is made up of various types of fruit and berries, and they can be destructive to fruit crops, particularly cherries. Acorns and beechnuts are also eaten, and may be stored in large quantities for winter use.

The Red-headed Woodpecker usually nests in the dead top of a deciduous tree or a rotting stump from which the bark has peeled. In the prairie areas where trees are scarce, telephone poles are frequently used. The birds excavate cavities or sometimes use natural cavities, which may be anywhere from one to 24 metres in height. The eggs are pure white in color and are laid directly on the wood chips in the bottom of the cavity. Both the male and female birds assist in incubating the eggs and feeding the young birds, which remain in the nest for almost four weeks.

The young are blind and naked when hatched, but by the time they leave the nest they are completely feathered, and although similarly patterned, look very different from the adults. Instead of the adult red coloring about the head and breast they are brownish gray and the white wing feathers are patterned or barred with black. The underparts are tinged brownish and the black is not glossy. They begin to molt these feathers in early autumn and slowly continue throughout the winter. By May they have a fully adult plumage. Adults have a complete molt in late summer.

In all plumages both sexes look alike.

These birds often seem to have little fear of man allowing a close approach.

Total length: Males 220-245mm (8.7-9.7in). Females 220-245mm (8.7-9.7in)
Wing length: Males 132-142mm (5.2-5.6in). Females 131-138mm (5.15-5.4in)
Wing span: Males 360-430mm (14.2-16.9in). Females 350-420mm (13.8-16.5in)
Weight: Males 60-85g (2-3oz). Females 68-78g (2.4-2.75oz)

Breeding dates: May-June
Incubation period: 14 days
Number of eggs: 5 (4-7)

Preferred habitat: Open woodlots, farms

Red-headed Woodpecker

White

CCOATES

Gray Jay

Perisoreus canadensis

From Alaska to Newfoundland, south to New York and New Mexico, these birds are found wherever there are spruce and fir. The Gray Jay is not a migratory bird and hence is unknown outside its forest home. None the less, it is probably known to most people as it has been widely illustrated and written about under its former name — the Canada Jay.

Their diet consists of almost anything. In summer they are largely insectivorous, eating grasshoppers, beetles, bees, tent caterpillars and other insects. They may eat the eggs of other birds or even chase a woodpecker from a newly opened tree. They consume all types of berries, and in winter even eat lichens and the leaves of fir trees. Every camper or trapper who has spent time in the north woods knows that they will take food from tables, plates or even tents and cabins. Any kind of food left unprotected may be eaten or damaged, and what cannot be eaten immediately is stored in holes and crevices in trees for future use.

These jays are at times perhaps the boldest of birds. Showing little fear of man, they will readily approach any traveler in the forest. The slightest noise or disturbance will arouse their curiosity and bring them to see what is happening or if food is available.

They nest very early in the year when the snow is still deep in the forests and thus few people have been able to observe their nests. Like other jays, the Gray becomes very quiet and secretive during the nesting season – unlike its behavior at other times.

Nests are placed in small coniferous trees and built of sticks and moss, thickly lines with large quantities of plant down or feathers, to help protect the eggs and young from the freezing temperatures of late winter. Eggs are usually gray to greenish-white, evenly covered with small spots of olive-green. The female incubates the eggs alone, but the male brings most of the food for the young, allowing the female to remain on the nest to keep them warm.

After about two weeks, when the young leave the nest, they are covered with a fluffy slate-gray juvenal plumage which they keep until the middle of summer. Then they molt to a plumage which is essentially the same as that of the adult. Adult males and females, which look alike, molt their soft fluffy plumage once a year in summer.

Gray Jays seldom engage in long flights, but glide quietly through the forest from tree to tree. They hop from branch to branch up through a tree until gaining sufficient height to glide to another tree. Their calls, which consist of a variety of clear penetrating whistles or cries are seldom heard by humans.

Total length: Males 265-315mm (10.2-12.5in). Females 255-300mm (10-12in)
Wing length: Males 130-150mm (5-6in). Females 130-145mm (5-5.7in)
Wing span: Males 390-445mm (15-17.5in). Females 370-420mm (14.5-16.5in)
Weight: Males 70-85g (2.5-3oz). Females 60-80g (2.1-2.8oz)

Breeding dates: March-April
Incubation period: 16-18 days
Number of eggs: 3-4

Preferred habitat: Coniferous forest

Gray Jay

Blue Jay
Cyanocitta cristata

They are the only jays found over most of the settled parts of eastern North America. Most of those living in Canada migrate south, but a number of these strikingly beautiful birds remain in their breeding areas throughout the winter. Although birds of the forest, they have adapted well to man's presence, and are readily attracted to feeding stations, at times even nesting in city gardens and ravines.

Their diet consists of almost anything edible, be it plant or animal. Although the eggs of snails, frogs, mice and birds are consumed, the bulk of the animal material consists of insects including such pests as beetles, grasshoppers, caterpillars and weevils. However, grains, wild berries, nuts and fruit of most any type comprise nearly three quarters of their food.

Although Blue Jays prefer to live in mixed forests, their nests are most often placed on branches in dense coniferous thickets. Sticks, leaves, bark and grass form the raw materials of these nests, which are lined with fine rootlets. The eggs are generally an olive buff color, with small spots of dull brown scattered evenly over the surface. The female does most of the incubating, but the male assists in both incubating and feeding the young, which remain in the nest nearly three weeks.

The young birds are naked when hatched, but by the time they leave the nest are fully-feathered and able to fly. The juvenal plumage is similar to that of the adults, but the crown and back is grayer and the black markings are less intense. A few months after leaving the nest the young molt all their body plumage and are then nearly identical to the adult birds in appearance. Adults molt all plumage once a year in summer.

Their loud ringing "jay" call is a commonly heard sound throughout the eastern woodlands in autumn and is the best-known of their many calls. This song may be used as an alarm, warning the other forest animals of the approach of man. In and around its nest, however, the Blue Jay is a very quiet and secretive bird.

Total length: Males 260-320mm (10-12.5in). Females 270-300mm (10.5-12in)
Wing length: Males 130-145mm (5.1-5.7in). Females 130-140mm (5.1-5.5in)
Wing span: Males 380-450mm (15.2-17.7in). Females 390-430mm (15.4-17in)
Weight: Males 85-110g (3-3.9oz). Females 80-105g (2.8-3.7oz)

Breeding dates: April-July
Incubation period: 17-18 days
Number of eggs: 4-6

Preferred habitat: Woodland

Blue Jay

Steller's Jay

Cyanocitta stelleri

The western counterpart of
the eastern Blue Jay, they range from Alaska to Central America. Throughout their
territory 13 subspecies are recognized.
As with most jays, Steller's Jays are omnivorous, eating both animal and vegetable matter.
They consume a variety of insects including grasshoppers, crickets, beetles, caterpillars, moths, bees
and spiders. They will also eat frogs, the remains of dead animals, and the eggs of other birds.
Among the vegetable food are prunes, cherries, berries, grains and nuts. In some cases
they may be destructive to grain or nut crops, but the bulk of their food is
insects and wild fruit.
They inhabit primarily mountainous, coniferous forests, but in the south venture into orchards
and farms. Their nests are usually placed in low coniferous trees, on horizontal branches near the trunk.
The nests are bulky, constructed of sticks, and lined with fine rootlets and grasses. The eggs are a pale
bluish-green, evenly marked with brownish spots. The incubating bird sits quietly until approached
very closely, then makes a terrific outcry before silently leaving the area until the intruder departs.
Both the male and female share in the duties of building the nest, incubating
the eggs and feeding the young.
The young birds are nearly naked when hatched, but, by the time they are ready to leave the nest,
are feathered with a dark sooty-gray plumage. Only their wings and tail are blue as in adults. This plumage
is molted in late summer – when the adults also molt – and then all ages are similarly colored.
Male and female plumage is identical.
Steller's Jays are well-known as nest robbers and the other small birds of the forest are quick
to chase and scold these jays on sight during the nesting season. Like Blue Jays, they have a variety of
calls, and also a similar habit of sounding a warning when an intruder approaches, while they remain
hidden from potential harm. Their "alert" or "jay" call is more nasal and harsh than the ringing
call of the Blue Jay. The calls of hawks are ably imitated by this species.
Young and adults may stay together as a family group through most of the summer, but in
early autumn disperse and wander widely. In general they do not migrate, but some of the more
northern birds often travel south, and those nesting at higher elevations may move
lower into the valleys for the winter.

Total length: Males 290-335mm (11.5-13in). Females 290-330mm (11.5-13in)
Wing length: Males 144-150mm (5.7-5.9in). Females 140-150mm (5.5-5.9in)
Wing span: Males 425-480mm (17-19in). Females 435-475mm (17-19in)
Weight: Males 90-125g (3.2-4.4oz). Females 85-120g (3-4.2oz)

Breeding dates: April-June
Incubation period: 16-18 days
Number of eggs: 4 (3-5)

Preferred habitat: Mixed forest

Steller's Jay

Black-capped Chickadee

Parus atricapillus

This bird is a member of the Titmouse family, which is comprised of many species found around the world, principally in the Northern Hemisphere. Generally non-migratory, these tiny birds brave Canada's cold northern winters, and are perhaps the best known of Canada's winter birds. They readily visit bird feeders and are trusting enough to take food from one's hand.

Most of their nourishment consists of animal matter. In winter they consume a high proportion of insect eggs, helping to reduce the insect pests of orchards, gardens and farms. In summer they feed on tent caterpillars, spiders, beetles, moths, bugs, scale insects, ants, saw flies and plant lice in egg, larval or adult form. Various nuts, seeds and wild fruits make up the vegetable portion of their diet.

The Black-capped Chickadee's usual nesting site is a cavity in a dead stub or branch, usually close to the ground. This cavity may be natural but most often is excavated in the soft rotting wood by the birds themselves. Both male and female help in the excavation, carefully carrying away the wood chips. Plant down, hair, moss, feathers, and insect cocoons, placed in the excavated hole, make up the nest material.

The eggs are white and evenly marked with very fine spots of reddish brown. They are incubated only by the female, but the male brings food to his incubating mate and assists in raising the young. The nestlings remain in the nest cavity for just over two weeks.

The young have a mouse-gray, natal down at hatching but this is soon replaced with the juvenal plumage. Except for a short tail, they look much like adult birds when they leave the nest, but the plumage is fluffier and the black coloration is much duller. In the late summer the body plumage molts and the young become nearly indistinguishable from adults. It is at this time that the adults also have a complete molt of feathers.

Chickadees spend the winter in small flocks roving about woodlands or gardens, searching the branches of evergreens or deciduous trees for food. They are constantly calling to keep in contact with each other, often singing the familiar *chicka-dee-dee-dee* call from which their name is derived.

Total length: Males 125-140mm (4.9-5.5in). Females 120-140mm (4.7-5.5in)
Wing length: Males 65-70mm (2.6-2.8in). Females 60-65mm (2.4-2.6in)
Wing span: Males 190-210mm (7.5-8.3in). Females 180-210mm (7.0-8.3in)
Weight: Males 10-13g (.35-.46oz). Females 10-12g (.35-.42oz)

Breeding dates: May-June
Incubation period: 12-13 days
Number of eggs: 6-8

Preferred habitat: Woodland

Black-capped Chickadee

Red-breasted Nuthatch
Sitta canadensis

his tiny bird is perhaps not well known in its summer home among our northern spruce forests. But with the coming of winter they pour forth from the secluded forests and pass in considerable numbers through more southern woodlots, parks and gardens. Their nasal call notes can be heard long before they are seen. When seen they are busily climbing about the branches and trunks of trees, seldom remaining stationary for long. Lacking the stiff tail feathers of woodpeckers and creepers to support them in a upright position, they are more often seen coming down the trunks of trees head first. Scurrying over the bark, their keen eyes are ever searching for the eggs and larvae of insects which make up a substantial portion of their diets. Adult insects of many kinds, weed seeds, and even bits of rotten apple or the sap of trees may also be consumed. They are fond of the seeds of fir, spruce and pine. When large seeds are found they are wedged into a crevice in the bark and pecked apart. These birds are also known to store seeds when abundant, for later use. The Red-breasted Nuthatch usually excavates a cavity in a rotted stub or branch of a dead tree. However, they sometimes use an old woodpecker hole or even a nest box. These cavities are chosen at almost any height, but usually well above the ground. They are lined with bark, grasses, moss, and feathers. A characteristic of all their nests is the presence of pitch smeared about the entrance to the cavity. It has been suggested that they smear this pitch around the hole to repel predators, but the real function remains a mystery. Because of the presence of this sticky substance the birds can sometimes be seen flying directly into the hole without so much as touching the edge. Both sexes assist in incubating the eggs which are white, spotted with reddish brown. The young are born with but a small bit of dark gray natal down. The juvenal plumage which is aquired before they leave the nest is similar to that of the adult plumage but is much duller. The body plumage is molted in late summer, and then the young appear nearly identical to adults. Adults also have a complete molt each year in late summer. Not all Red-breasted Nuthatches migrate south for the winter, and those which remain are readily attracted to feeding stations. The antics of this busy little bird are a most welcome sight in the cool days of winter.

Total length: Males 10.5-12.2mm (4.1-4.8in). Females 10.5-12.2mm (4.1-4.8in)
Wing length: Males 66-69mm (2.6-2.7in). Females 64-68mm (2.5-2.7in)
Wing span: Males 195-220mm (7.7-8.7in). Females 200-205mm (7.9-8.1in)
Weight: Males 8-11g (.28-.39oz). Females 8-11g (.28-.39oz)

Breeding dates: May-June
Incubation period: 12 days
Number of eggs: 5-6 (4-7)

Preferred habitat: Coniferous forest

Red-breasted Nuthatch

G. LOATES

Brown Creeper
Certhia familiaris

Although found in considerable
numbers throughout much of the Canadian forests in summer, these birds are seen to best advantage
when they move to and from the forests with the coming and receding of winter. These tiny birds, which
appear like a small flake of bark against a tree, are difficult to observe at the best of times. They have
only a faint thin call which might attract the attention of an observer. They scurry vertically up the trunks of
trees in search of food, using their long stiff tails to help support them. When they reach a considerable
height they fly down to the bottom of another tree and begin their climb again. But on their
descent to the base of another tree they could be mistaken for
nothing more than a falling leaf.
When busily searching for food they may seem quite oblivious to an approaching person
and allow one to walk very close to them. Unlike woodpeckers, they do not chisel away at trees but use
their long slender bills to probe deftly among the crevices for items which they have seen. Their food
consists of the eggs, larvae, or adults of a great variety of insects. Almost any insect which might
be found on the bark of trees is food for the creeper. Many of these insects are injurious to
the trees and many are so small as to be overlooked by other species of birds.
Creepers place their nests in narrow crevices between a loose sheaf of bark and a dead or live
tree trunk. Such well concealed nests are seldom seen, for they are not exposed nor are there any obvious
holes leading to the nest as with woodpeckers. The nest is loosely formed of grasses and lichens and
warmly lined with feathers. The eggs are a pure white, sparingly spotted with fine brown spots.
The young spend about two weeks in the nest and are able to climb tree trunks
as soon as they leave the nest.
Young birds are sparsely covered with a gray down at hatching but before they leave the nest
they have acquired a plumage which, although paler and less distinctly marked, is otherwise similar to
that of the adult bird. Their body plumage is molted again in late summer and the young are then
all but indistinguishable from the adults which have just completed
a molt of all their feathers.
Although most birds move south for the winter a few may remain in breeding areas.
On cold nights these birds are known to gather in groups, often in a natural cavity. Here they
crowd together to help conserve heat through the cold night.

Total length: Males 12.7-14.6mm (5-5.75in). Females 12.7-14.6mm (5-5.75in)
Wing length: Males 62-68mm (2.4-2.7in). Females 62-67mm (2.4-2.6in)
Wing span: Males 185-205mm (7.3-8.1in). Females 180-195mm (7.1-7.7in)
Weight: Males 7.5-10g (.26-.35oz). Females 8-11g (.28-.39oz)

Breeding dates: April-June
Incubation period: 14-15 days
Number of eggs: 5-6 (4-8)

Preferred habitat: Mixed forest

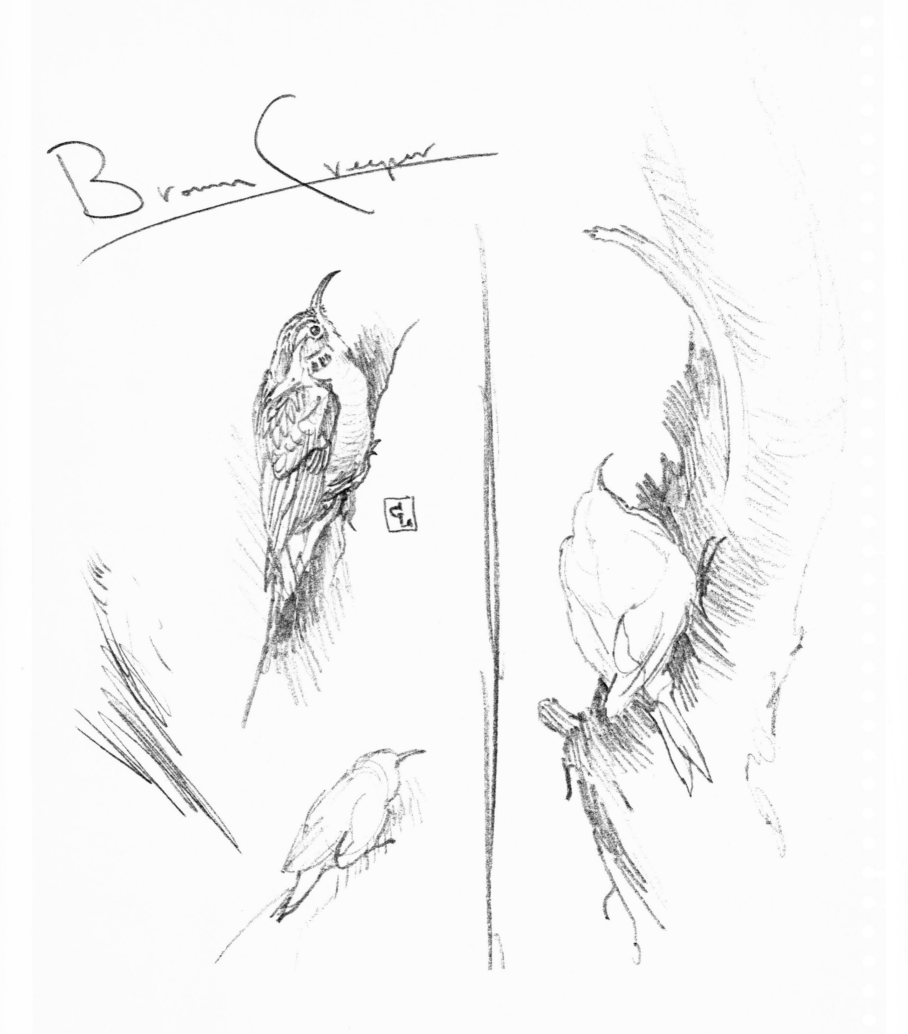

American Robin
Turdus migratorius

A member of a very large,
worldwide family of birds known as thrushes, the Robin is the largest thrush in North America
and is the best known as it has adapted readily to life in gardens and parks. It is one of the
earliest spring migrants, arriving in the north as soon as there is
bare ground where it may hunt for food.
Robins eat a great many wild fruits from dogwood, sumacs and cedars, berries of all types,
cherries and wild grapes. Where wild fruit is not available, they may become a nuisance in orchards
and gardens. They also consume beetles, grasshoppers, caterpillars, earthworms, bugs, wasps,
cutworms and many other insects as well as snails, sowbugs, and spiders.
Nests are placed in a variety of situations, even under eaves or on window sills, but most often
in trees on a horizontal branch or the crotch of a limb. The nest, which may be very low to the ground
or very high, is composed of coarse grasses and mud, forming a solid cup which is lined with
fine grasses. The birds begin nesting early in spring and
three or four nests may be made in one year.
The eggs are an unmarked, pale blue color. Only the female incubates the eggs,
but the males assist in feeding the young. The young remain in the nest just over two weeks,
after which time the female begins building a new nest, leaving the care of
the young to the male parent.
Nestlings have a sparse amount of mouse-gray down upon hatching. The juvenal plumage is
considerably different from the adult plumage—the back is more brownish with some white spotting,
and the underparts are whitish on the throat and abdomen and a pale rufous color spotted
with black on the breast. In late summer the young molt all body feathers and look
much like adults, although somewhat browner or grayer. Adults also undergo
an annual molt of all feathers in late summer.
Robins nesting in gardens may become quite aggressive in defense of their young
and very noisy at the approach of a person or animal. However, most of us are more familiar
with the beautiful caroling of both morning and evening, beginning before
sunrise and ending long after sunset.

Total length: Males 230-270mm (9.1-10.6in). Females 230-270mm (9.1-10.6in)
Wing length: Males 125-135mm (4.9-5.3in). Females 120-135mm (4.7-5.3in)
Wing span: Males 360-420mm (14.1-16.5in). Females 350-405mm (13.8-15.9in)
Weight: Males 75-90g (2.6-3.2oz). Females 60-100g (2.1-3.5oz)

Breeding dates: April-August
Incubation period: 12-14 days
Number of eggs: 3-5

Preferred habitat: Gardens, open woodland

Every year I look forward
to the coming of spring, for
with it comes the robin, one
of my favourite birds. Its
fondness for human society, has
made it probably the best
known bird in
this country.

EQ OATES - 1977

Robin

Fall plumage tipped
with white.

Golden-crowned Kinglet

Regulus satrapa

These tiny balls of feathers are
the lesser known of the two kinglets of North America. They make their summer home in the
spruce forests, spending most of their time in the tops of the trees. Since many spend the winter in the
breeding areas there is not a sudden great migration. Most wander slowly southward for the winter and back
north in spring. At such times they wander into more open woods and shrubbery where we may more
easily watch them incessantly searching every little twig for a morsel of food. The orange center
in the male's crown is often difficult to detect, because he spreads it to full view only when excited.
Young birds do not have the colored crown and could be mistaken for Ruby-crowned Kinglets,
except that they lack the white ring about the eye.
The diet of the Golden-crowned Kinglet appears to be almost entirely made up of insects.
They glean eggs and larvae from branches and twigs, and no item is too small for these sharp-eyed little birds.
In spring they may be attracted to the sap of trees, either for the sap itself or for the tiny insects which are
attracted as well. Small spiders, scale insects, flies and numerous other
tiny creatures are all eagerly consumed.
The nest of the Golden-crowned Kinglet is a small globular ball of moss formed and
suspended by spider webs and insect silk, in a dense cluster of twigs. It is well concealed in foliage, almost
invariably in an evergreen tree, and usually high above the ground. The nest is thick walled and
open at the top but usually lined with many feathers to help keep the eggs and young warm.
The tiny eggs are white, sprinkled with numerous pale brown spots. Large clutches
of eggs are laid, and in such tiny nests they cannot all lie on the nest bottom,
but form two layers. Both sexes assist in rearing the young, but only
the female incubates the eggs.
The newly hatched kinglets are blind and have but a few tufts of gray down. When ready
to leave the nest they look nearly like the adults except that they lack the brightly colored crown.
A molt in late summer replaces all body plumage and except for the worn wing feathers they
become identical to the adults in appearance. Adults have but a single annual molt
of all their feathers in late summer.
Such tiny birds are constantly searching for food, yet no item is too small,
and no twig is too small to support their weight. They must surely be of great benefit
in controlling insect infestations on our forests.

Total length: Males 8.7-10mm (3.5-4in). Females 8.7-10mm (3.5-4in)
Wing length: Males 54-59mm (2.1-2.3in). Females 53-56mm (2.1-2.2in)
Wing span: Males 165-180mm (6.5-7.1in). Females 165-180mm (6.5-7.1in)
Weight: Males 5.3-7.0g (.185-.25oz). Females 5.2-7.0g (.18-.25oz)

Breeding dates: April-July
Incubation period: ? ? ?
Number of eggs: 8-9 (5-10)

Preferred habitat: Coniferous forest

Golden-crowned Kinglet

Ruby-crowned Kinglet

Regulus calendula

Few people who spend time in
our vast boreal forests in early summer can fail to encounter this bird. For although it is
but a tiny creature it has a most remarkable song, which in volume surpasses that of birds many times its size.
This rich warbling song, however, is seldom ever heard in spring or autumn when they are migrating.
Although a rather nondescript color, they are not difficult to see in autumn, for there are many
thousands passing southward for the winter. They are surely one of our most common
songbirds. In winter, few remain as far north as Canada but
some will linger late into autumn.
Their diet is almost entirely made up of such insects as wasps, ants, bugs, lice, scale insects,
caterpillars of all types and spiders. They also eat some small fruits and seeds.
The nest of the Ruby-crowned Kinglet is almost always high in a spruce tree, suspended among
a dense clump of pendant twigs, often near the end of a branch. It forms a deep cup composed of mosses and
lichens, held together with insect silk and spider webs, and lined with feathers, hair, plant down
or finely shredded bark. The entrance to the nest is like a short tube
nearly closed by the feather lining.
The eggs, laid in large clutches, are white with fine spots of brown. It is difficult to
imagine how such a tiny bird can incubate so many eggs. The thick-walled warmly lined nest must be
of considerable help in retaining heat. Only the female incubates,
but both sexes assist in bringing food to the young.
The young are nearly naked when hatched. After about two weeks, when they leave the nest,
they have a plumage like that of the adult female but browner in color. In late summer they molt their
body plumage at the time the adults are undergoing their complete annual molt. The young and
adults then appear similar, but young males lack the scarlet crown patch.
The kinglets are little bundles of energy, constantly flitting about in their never-ending search
for food. They loudly scold all who come too near, but their seeming enthusiasm
is always welcome.

Total length: Males 9.4-11.4mm (3.7-4.5in). Females 9.4-11.4mm (3.7-4.5in)
Wing length: Males 56-61mm (2.2-2.4in). Females 54-58mm (2.1-2.3in)
Wing span: Males 170-185mm (6.7-7.3in). Females 165-180mm (6.5-7.1in)
Weight: Males 6-8g (.21-.28oz). Females 5.5-7.5g (.19-.26oz)

Breeding dates: May-July
Incubation period: ? ? ?
Number of eggs: 7-9 (5-11)

Preferred habitat: Coniferous woodland

Ruby-crowned Kinglet

Ruby red not always seen

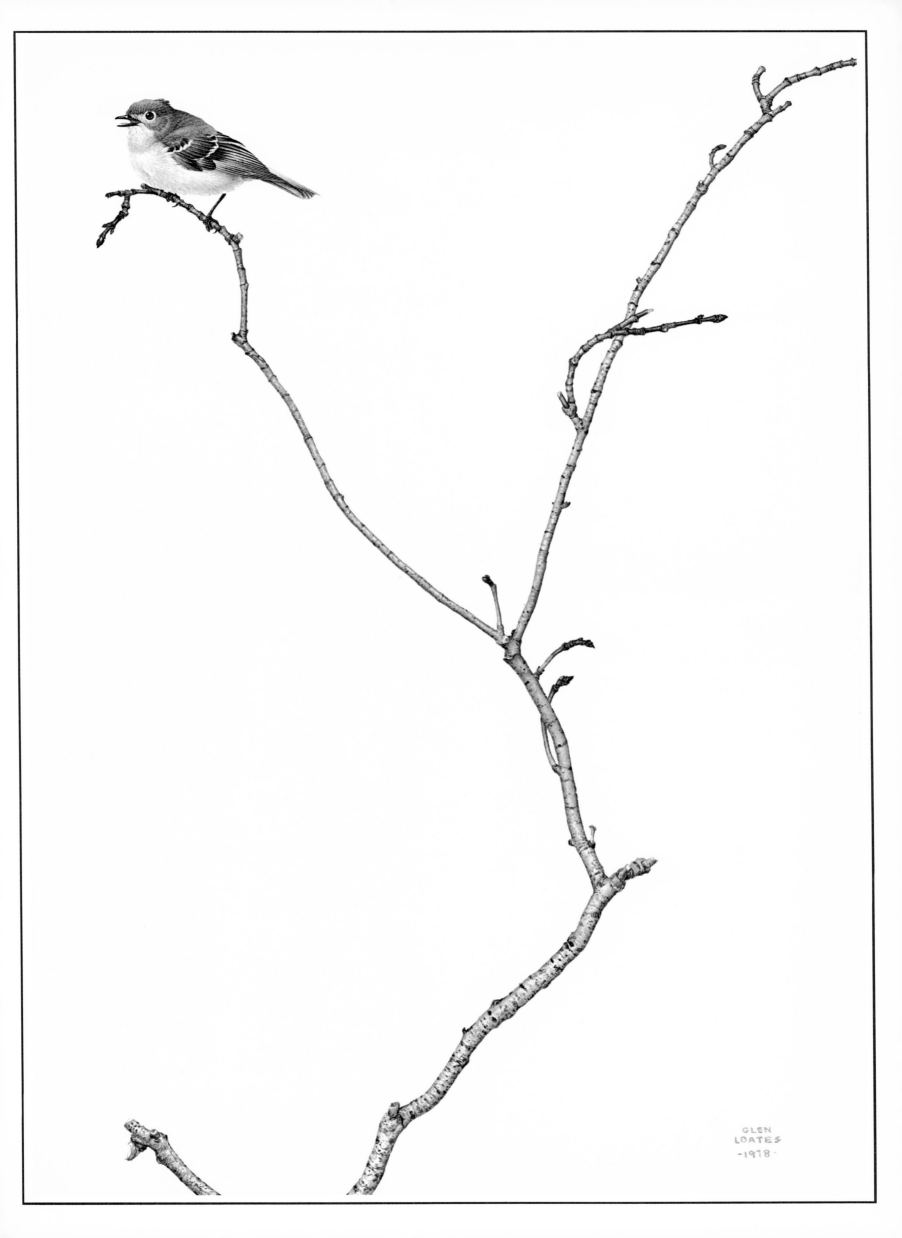

GLEN
LOATES
-1978-

Cedar Waxwing

Bombycilla cedrorum

A very small family of birds consisting of only three members, Waxwings breed across the continent from southeastern Alaska to Newfoundland, south to the northern United States and to northern Georgia in the eastern mountains, and northern California in the western mountains. They are not migratory in the usual sense, wintering as far north as southern Canada. Some, however, do wander south as far as Central America.

About 80 per cent of their food is vegetable matter, mostly wild berries and cherries, but also the flowers of many kinds of trees. In orchards, they occasionally eat flowers or fruit, but may also consume a variety of insects injurious to these orchards if flowers or ripe cherries are not available. They are adept at catching insects on the wing and consume enormous numbers of flying insects in this fashion.

The bird's name is derived from the small wax-like appendages which tip a number of the secondary wing feathers. The soft browns, grays, and yellows of adult birds, set off with a touch of red on the wings and a black facial mask make the Waxwings particularly distinguished-looking.

In winter the birds wander about in flocks, and may be late arrivals in their breeding areas. Once they have returned to their summer haunts, they do not immediately set about nesting. Waxwings nest much later than most birds, at a time when many berries and other fruits will be ripe to feed their young. The nests, placed in bushes and small trees, consist of twigs, grass and weed stalks fitted loosely together and lined more compactly with rootlets, fine grasses, plant down and feathers. Both parents assist in building the nest, but only the female incubates the eggs. The latter are a pale, bluish-gray color, with black spots sparingly scattered over the whole surface.

The young Waxwings hatch without natal down. The female broods, while the male brings food, until the young become partially feathered. By the time the young leave the nest after about two weeks, they are almost fully feathered. Except for a more prominent white line above the eye, lack of red wax on the wings and heavy streaking below, the young have plumage colors closely resembling those of the adults. They molt all body plumage in September and then are nearly identical in appearance to the adults. Adult males and females also look alike and undergo a complete molt in September.

Cedar Waxwings do not actively defend territories, although the large, winter flocks disperse so that pairs are generally well spreadout for nesting. However, they often nest in close proximity, and are tolerant both of each other and of birds of other species. In keeping with their social habits, their call is a high-pitched, long clear whistle, scarcely audible except at close range, rather than a loud call more suitable for proclaiming a territory or repelling a rival.

Total length: Males 150-195mm (5.9-7.7in). Females 155-190mm (6.1-7.5in)
Wing length: Males 91-98mm (3.6-3.9in). Females 89-97mm (3.5-3.9in)
Wing span: Males 270-305mm (10.6-12.0in). Females 270-300mm (10.6-11.8in)
Weight: Males 30-42g (1.1-1.5oz). Females 29-40g (1.1-1.4oz)

Breeding dates: June-September
Incubation period: 12 days
Number of eggs: 3-5

Preferred habitat: Open woodland

Cedar Waxwing

COATES

M. G. LOATES - 1974 -

Canada Warbler
Wilsonia canadensis

This warbler belongs to that family of wood warblers found only in the Western Hemisphere, a beautiful little bird that prefers to live in mixed forests where there is a great deal of undergrowth. It is not seen very often in summer in these dense woods, where mosquitoes and blackflies abound, but is a common migrant in eastern North America, flying to and from its wintering areas in northern South America.

The Warbler's food consists of flies, moths, beetles, grubs, caterpillars, and the eggs of insects, spiders, mosquitoes, and other flying insects. They search on the branches and foliage of trees and on the ground for food, a good deal of which they also take in flight in the manner of flycatchers.

For the most part, nests are built on the ground, but may be placed on moss-covered stumps or on the upturned roots of a fallen tree. Usually they are found well within the dense layers of moss of wet woodlands, and have a small entrance at the side. The nest itself is made up of leaves, bark fibers, and soft pine needles, lined with fine bark fibers and rootlets.

The eggs are creamy-white, spotted and speckled with chestnut brown. The markings are generally concentrated in a ring about the larger end of the eggs. Apparently the female does all the incubating of the eggs and brooding of the young, but the male does assist in feeding. The young probably remain in the nest about two weeks although little is known about their nesting patterns.

The newly-hatched nestlings have a light brown natal down. This is soon replaced with a juvenal plumage which is a light brown above and yellow with some pale brown wash below. They molt their body plumage again in late summer and then look much like adults except that the black markings are grayer and much less distinct. This plumage is retained until the second autumn when a full adult plumage is acquired. Both adults and young may molt a few feathers about the head and neck in spring, but have only one annual molt of all feathers. The female looks like the male, with somewhat less vivid markings.

Total length: Males 125-150mm (4.9-5.9in). Females 125-145mm (4.9-5.7in)
Wing length: Males 60-70mm (2.4-2.7in). Females 60-70mm (2.4-2.7in)
Wing span: Males 185-200mm (7.2-7.8in). Females 175-190mm (6.9-7.5in)
Weight: Males 9-12g (.32-.42oz). Females 9-12g (.32-.42oz)

Breeding dates: May-June
Incubation period: 12-14 days
Number of eggs: 3-5

Preferred habitat: Shrubby undergrowth of woodlands

House Sparrow
Passer domesticus

The House or English Sparrow does not belong to the same family as the native North American sparrow, but is, rather, a Weaver Finch, native to Europe, Asia and Africa. They were introduced to North America in the mid 19th century. House Sparrows proved so adaptable that they spread rapidly across the continent. At present they are permanent residents throughout the heavily-settled parts of the country, with isolated colonies north to the North-West Territories, central Quebec and Newfoundland and south through most of Mexico.

Being largely grain-eating birds they were able to pick up grain dropped from transport vehicles along roads and railways – they even found transportation on train cars to more distant places. This accelerated their spread across the country, so that in only 40 years from the first introduction, they had colonized most of their present range. During the late 19th century, when the use of horses was wide-spread, the grain fed to livestock provided the sparrows with much food. Today, with fewer horses in use, the birds are much less common in cities and towns, but are still found in rural areas in the vicinity of grain-fed livestock. Apart from grain, they feed on many types of weed and grass seeds and consume a number of insects, particularly in summer, to nourish nestlings.

The nests are big, bulky, loosely constructed bundles of grass placed almost anywhere that will conceal them to some degree. This may be holes and crevices in buildings and man-made structures, or among the branches of evergreen trees. House Sparrows are aggressive and often drive other birds from nest boxes, even to the point of taking over the nests of species like the Cliff Swallow.

The entrance to the nest is a small hole in the side, and the nest cavity is lined with feathers. The eggs are almost white with a faint greenish or bluish tint, and evenly spotted with fine gray spots. The female does all the incubating, but both parents assist in feeding the young, which remain in the nest for just over two weeks. The young are fed by their parents for a few weeks after leaving the nest, but after that, the parents begin to build a second nest and raise more young. Three or more broods may be raised in one season.

Young birds are born without natal down, but by six days their feathers begin to emerge. The juvenal plumage is a drab brown, not unlike that of the female. Five weeks after the young leave the nest, they molt to an adult plumage. The young molt again in late August, at the same time the adults undergo their annual molt.

The House Sparrow has long been considered the worst bird pest in North America and its introduction a great error. But today they are nowhere as common as they once were, and their incessant chirping adds a little cheer to our long winters when most other birds have left.

Total length: Males 135-165mm (5.3-6.5in). Females 130-160mm (5.1-6.3in)
Wing length: Males 74-79mm (2.9-3.1in). Females 72-78mm (2.8-3.1in)
Wing span: Males 225-255mm (8.9-10in). Females 220-255mm (8.7-10in)
Weight: Males 25-35g (0.9-1.2oz). Females 20-35g (0.7-1.2oz)

Breeding dates: April-July
Incubation period: 12 days
Number of eggs: 5 (3-7)

Preferred habitat: Urban areas, farms

Cardinal
Cardinalis cardinalis

One of our most beautiful and best-known seed-eating finches, the Cardinal formerly occupied only the southern areas of the United States, as well as parts of Mexico, but has moved northward in the east over the last century to become a fairly common sight as far north as South Dakota and southern Ontario.

As well as occupying streamside thickets and open woodlands with dense bushes, Cardinals move right into city gardens where there are sufficient shrubs and vines to provide them with a suitable habitat. As these birds do not migrate south in winter, they are easily attracted to winter bird feeders and in the summer make frequent use of bird baths.

Adult Cardinals eat mostly vegetable food, although nestlings are fed almost entirely on insects. Wild fruits of any kind, grass and weed seeds form most of the diet, while beetles, worms, grubs and many other insects are consumed.

Cardinals begin to sing long before the snows of winter have gone as they pair off and establish nesting territories. The song is a rapid repetition of loud, clear, flute-like notes. It is a beautiful song to hear in the late winter months. Both male and female sing as they court, displaying their bright red crests.

Nests are placed in bushes or small evergreens, usually about six feet from the ground. Built largely by the female, they are loosely constructed of sticks, grasses, leaves and bark strips, lined with fine rootlets. The eggs are whitish, and evenly speckled with brown. Incubation is normally performed by the female, but both parents feed the young. The latter remain in the nest about ten days. The nestlings, when hatched, are covered with a mouse-gray down. Before leaving the nest, they have acquired a covering of feathers which closely resembles the more drab olive-brown of the adult female. The young molt in late summer, at which time the males assume the bright red plumage of the adult. Adults also undergo their complete annual molt at this time.

The young are fed by their parents for as long as a month after leaving the nest. A new nest may be built before the young are fully independent, so that several broods may be raised in one season.

The combination of brilliant plumage, a rich and beautiful song, as well as food habits beneficial to man, make the Cardinal a very attractive addition to our gardens and farms.

Total length: Males 185-235mm (7.3-9.3in). Females 180-230mm (7.1-9.1in)
Wing length: Males 91-98mm (3.6-3.9in). Females 88-96mm (3.5-3.8in)
Wing span: Males 265-305mm (10.4-12in), Females 280-305mm (10.2-12in)
Weight: Males 35-52g (1.2-1.8oz). Females 30-52g (1.1-1.8oz)

Breeding dates: April-July
Incubation period: 12-13 days
Number of eggs: 3-4

Preferred habitat: Thickets

Cardinal

Cortés

American Goldfinch
Carduelis tristis

This bird belongs to a group of finches whose distribution stretches around the world. The Goldfinch is found across North America from southern Canada to northern Mexico, and within this range four subspecies are recognized. They winter throughout the breeding range, but some southern movement appears to take place. They spend most of the year in flocks wandering in search of food.

Their food consists primarily of seeds, including those of birch, alder, thistle, ragweed and dandelion, but seeds of all types may be consumed. However, Goldfinches also readily take a variety of caterpillars, eggs of plant lice, aphids and other noxious insects.

They remain in flocks, even though apparently paired, until summer is well-advanced and many of the plants which provide their favorite food have gone to seed. Goldfinches do not defend well-defined territories as do most species of birds. But where a good food supply is available, several pairs may nest near each other. The plant most important to them is the thistle. This provides not only an abundant supply of food, but also the down with which they line their nests. These nests are usually placed quite low, in a great variety of trees, shrubs or even in the thistle themselves. They are made of grasses and bark strips lined with plant down. The female does all the building although the male accompanies her and may carry material which she builds into the nest.

The eggs are a pale bluish-white color and are unmarked. They are incubated entirely by the female, but the male brings her food while she sits on the nest. The female broods the young for five or six days and again the male brings the food for the young and the female. Many seed-eating birds feed their young insects at first, particularly soft green worms. But the Goldfinch feeds mostly seeds which are regurgitated and partly digested. The young remain in the nest about two weeks.

The nestlings at hatching are covered with a light grayish down. Their juvenal plumage looks much like that of the adult female. Both young and adults undergo a complete molt in September at which time the males loose their bright yellow plumage. All birds then look much like the females in summer. In spring all birds molt their body feathers, with the males assuming their bright yellow plumage again.

Goldfinches are birds of the open country where they often travel about with flocks of other finches. The simple high-pitched notes, which they sing as they fly in a characteristically undulating flight, can be heard year round, adding notes of inspiration to an often dreary winter scene.

Total length: Males 105-130mm (4-5in). Females 100-130mm (4-5in)
Wing length: Males 70-74mm (2.7-2.9in). Females 67-74mm (2.6-2.9in)
Wing span: Males 175-230mm (6.9-9in). Females 170-225mm (6.7-8.9in)
Weight: Males 12-14.5g (0.4-0.5oz). Females 11.5-15g (0.4-0.5oz)

Breeding dates: July-September
Incubation period: 12-14 days
Number of eggs: 4-6

Preferred habitat: Overgrown fields

Am. Goldfinch

thic~ purple-pink

white wing bars

black
orange

lemon yellow

COATES

Distribution Maps

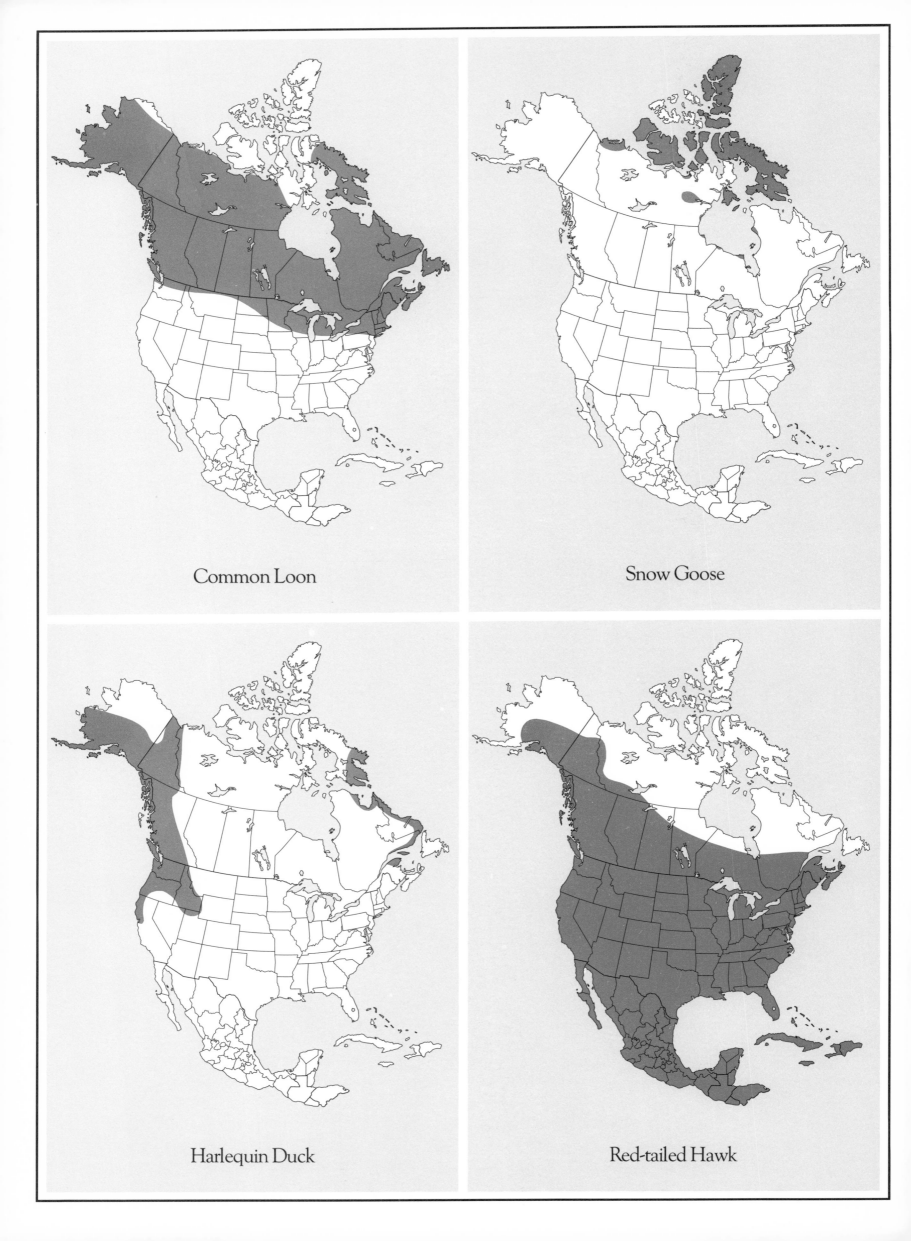

Common Loon

Snow Goose

Harlequin Duck

Red-tailed Hawk

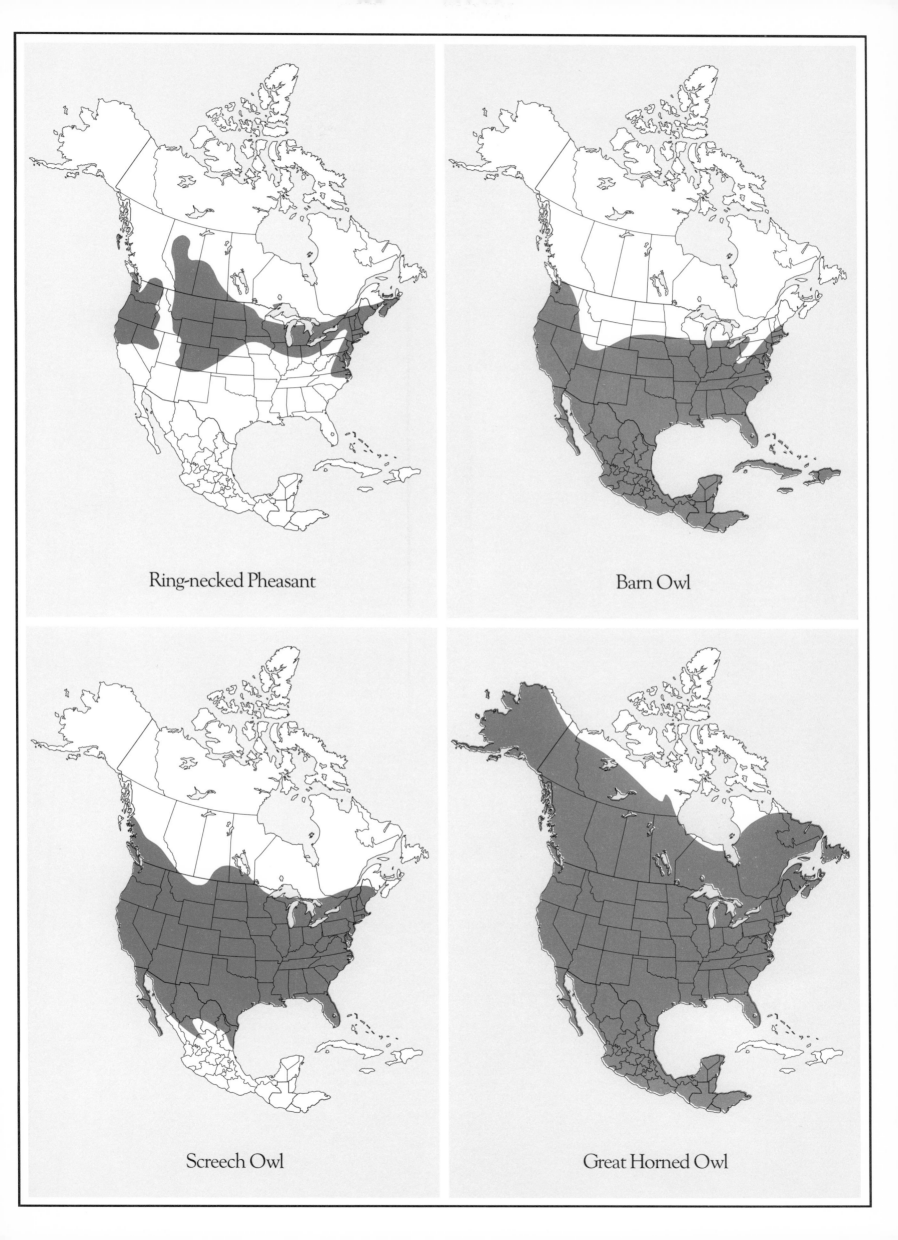

Ring-necked Pheasant

Barn Owl

Screech Owl

Great Horned Owl

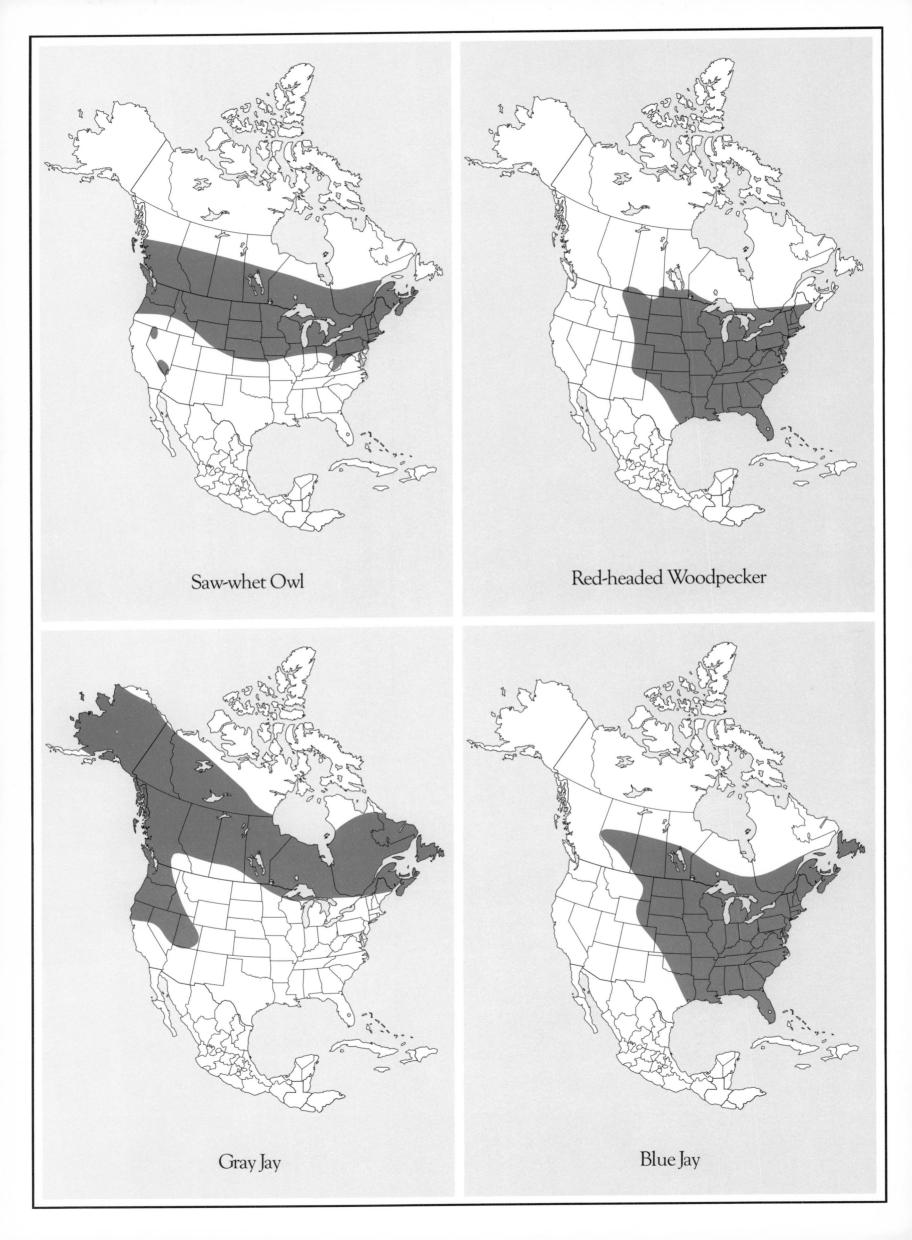

Saw-whet Owl

Red-headed Woodpecker

Gray Jay

Blue Jay

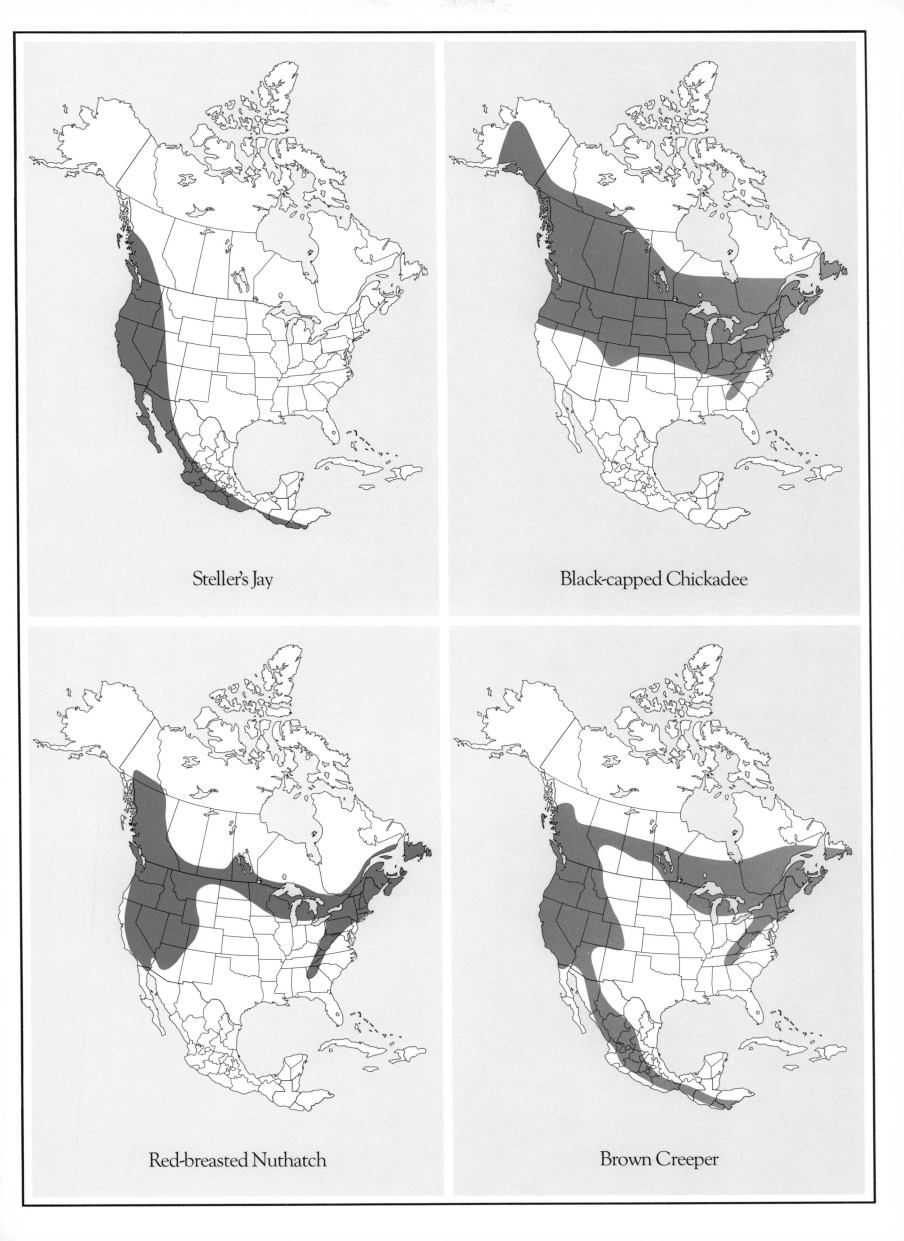

Steller's Jay

Black-capped Chickadee

Red-breasted Nuthatch

Brown Creeper

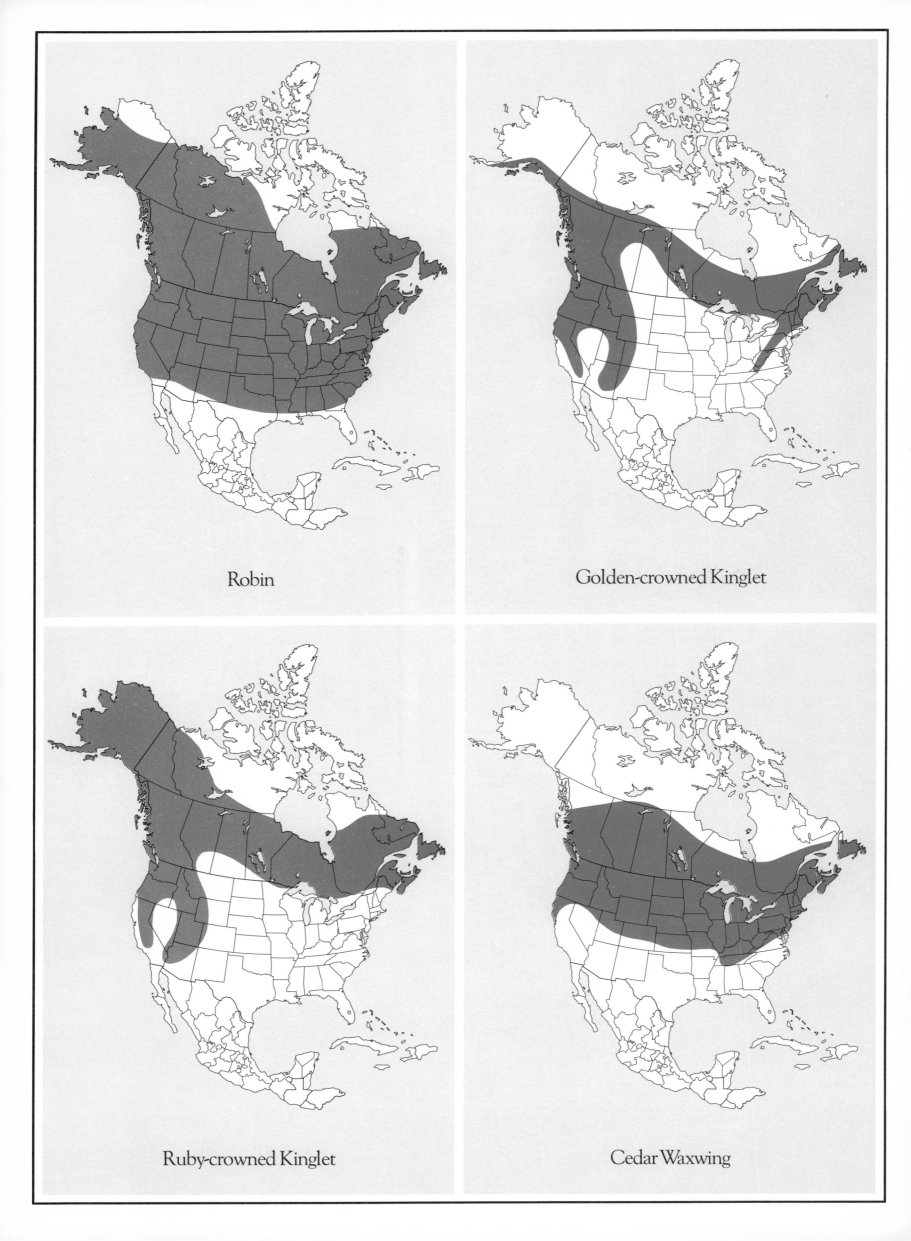

Robin

Golden-crowned Kinglet

Ruby-crowned Kinglet

Cedar Waxwing

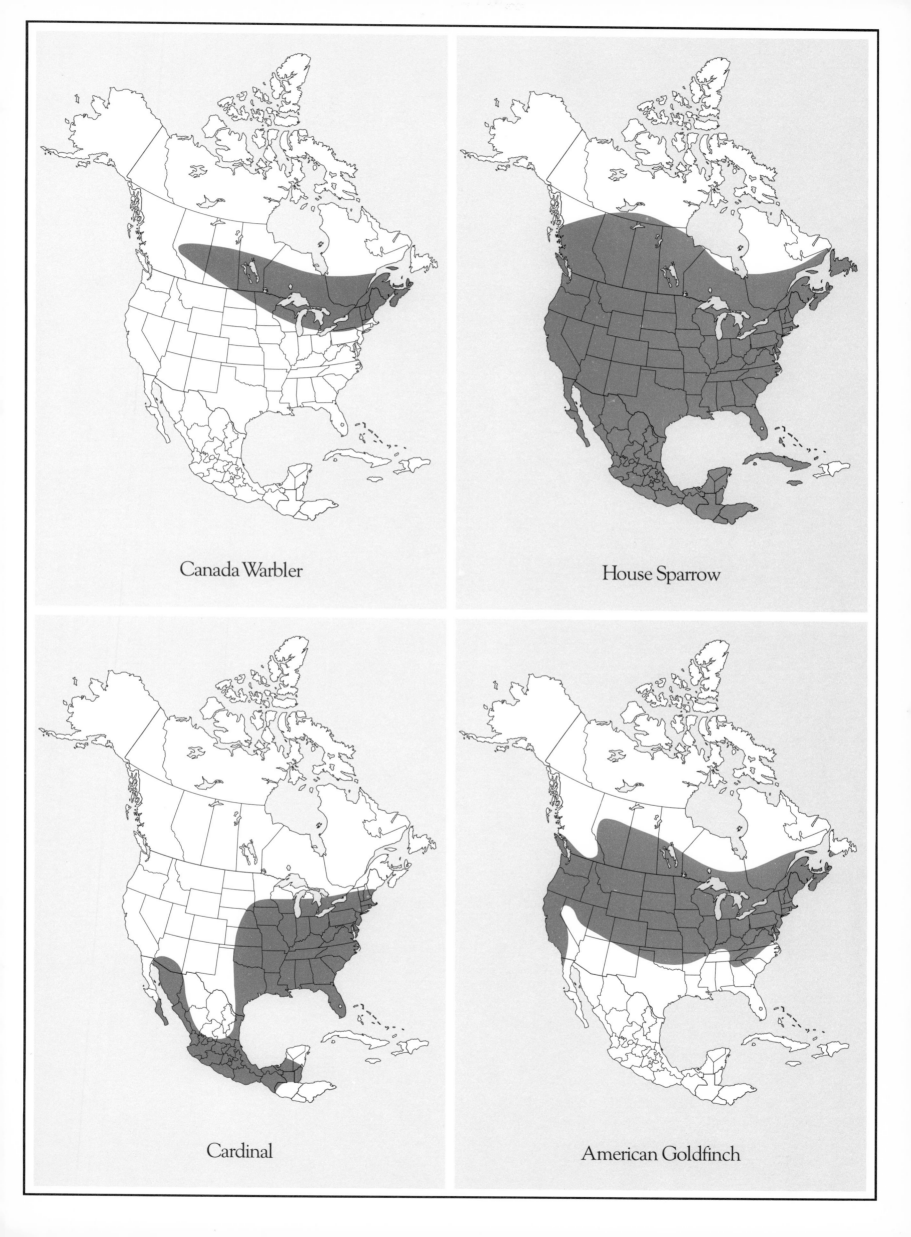

Canada Warbler

House Sparrow

Cardinal

American Goldfinch

Notice

Printed in Canada